ᗪISNEY
FROZEN

Disney Frozen

BREAKING BOUNDARIES

STORY & SCRIPT BY
JOE CARAMAGNA

ART BY
KAWAII CREATIVE STUDIOS

REUNION ROAD

STORY & SCRIPT BY
JOE CARAMAGNA

LAYOUTS BY
EDUARDO FRANCISCO

LINE ART BY
EDUARD PETROVICH

COLORING BY
YANA CHINSTOVA & ANASTASIIA BELOUSOVA

LETTERING BY
**RICHARD STARKINGS AND
COMICRAFT'S JIMMY BETANCOURT**

COVER ART BY
KAWAII CREATIVE STUDIOS

DARK HORSE BOOKS

DARK HORSE BOOKS

PRESIDENT AND PUBLISHER
MIKE RICHARDSON

EDITOR
FREDDYE MILLER

DESIGNER
BRENNAN THOME

ASSISTANT EDITORS
**JUDY KHUU, JENNY BLENK,
KEVIN BURKHALTER**

DIGITAL ART TECHNICIAN
SAMANTHA HUMMER

Neil Hankerson Executive Vice President Tom Weddle Chief Financial Officer Randy Stradley Vice President of Publishing Nick McWhorter Chief Business Development Officer Dale LaFountain Chief Information Officer Matt Parkinson Vice President of Marketing Cara Niece Vice President of Production and Scheduling Mark Bernardi Vice President of Book Trade and Digital Sales Ken Lizzi General Counsel Dave Marshall Editor in Chief Davey Estrada Editorial Director Chris Warner Senior Books Editor Cary Grazzini Director of Specialty Projects Lia Ribacchi Art Director Vanessa Todd-Holmes Director of Print Purchasing Matt Dryer Director of Digital Art and Prepress Michael Gombos Senior Director of International Publishing and Licensing Kari Yadro Director of Custom Programs Kari Torson Director of International Licensing Sean Brice Director of Trade Sales

DISNEY PUBLISHING WORLDWIDE GLOBAL MAGAZINES, COMICS AND PARTWORKS

PUBLISHER Lynn Waggoner • EDITORIAL TEAM Bianca Coletti (Director, Magazines), Guido Frazzini (Director, Comics), Carlotta Quattrocolo (Executive Editor), Stefano Ambrosio (Executive Editor, New IP), Camilla Vedove (Senior Manager, Editorial Development), Behnoosh Khalili (Senior Editor), Julie Dorris (Senior Editor), Mina Riazi (Assistant Editor) • DESIGN Enrico Soave (Senior Designer) • ART Ken Shue (VP, Global Art), Manny Mederos (Senior Illustration Manager, Comics and Magazines), Roberto Santillo (Creative Director), Marco Ghiglione (Creative Manager), Stefano Attardi (Illustration Manager) • PORTFOLIO MANAGEMENT Olivia Ciancarelli (Director) • BUSINESS & MARKETING Mariantonietta Galla (Senior Manager, Franchise), Virpi Korhonen (Editorial Manager)

Published by Dark Horse Books
A division of Dark Horse Comics LLC
10956 SE Main Street, Milwaukie, OR 97222

DarkHorse.com

To find a comics shop in your area, visit comicshoplocator.com

Scholastic edition: June 2019
ISBN 978-1-50671-537-7

1 3 5 7 9 10 8 6 4 2
Printed in Canada

Welcome to Arendelle!

Elsa

The queen of the kingdom of Arendelle and Anna's older sister. Elsa has the ability to create snow and ice. She is confident, composed, creative, and warmhearted.

Anna

The princess of Arendelle and Elsa's younger sister. Anna has faith in others and puts a positive spin on every situation. She is compassionate, fearless, and doesn't shy away from following her heart—no matter what.

OLAF

A snowman that Elsa brought to life. Olaf is a friend to all! He likes warm hugs and he is full of wonder and optimism— nothing can bring him down.

KRISTOFF

An ice harvester and the official ice master and deliverer of Arendelle. Raised by trolls in the mountains, he understands the importance of friends, family, and being true to yourself. He lives with his reindeer Sven.

SVEN

A reindeer and loyal best friend to Kristoff. They have regular conversations, and though Sven cannot communicate in words, sometimes Kristoff speaks for him. He enjoys carrots and lichen.

Disney

FROZEN

BREAKING BOUNDARIES

SO MANY CLOCKS TO PACK UP...

PART ONE

Fast Friends

JINGLE JANGLE

HELLO?

OH! I'M SORRY, BUT WE'RE *CLOSED*...

THAT'S WHY I'M *HERE*, MR. ALDRING. I BROUGHT YOU A GIFT.

PRINCESS ANNA!

ARE THOSE *LINGONBERRY MUFFINS?* MY *FAVORITE!* HOW DID YOU KNOW?

I HEARD YOU MENTION IT A WHILE BACK AND I TOOK A *MENTAL NOTE.* JUST IN CASE.

OH, ANNA. YOU ALWAYS KNOW JUST HOW TO LIFT THIS OLD MAN'S SPIRITS.

YOU'RE NOT *OLD*, MR. ALDRING.

THAT'S KIND OF YOU TO SAY, BUT MY *KNEES* AND MY *BACK* DISAGREE. THAT'S WHY I'VE DECIDED TO *RETIRE.*

WITHOUT MY HELGA, IT'S TOO MUCH WORK TO KEEP THE STORE OPEN.

BUT WHAT WILL BECOME OF THE STORE WHEN YOU LEAVE?

AND *YOU,* ANNA...

...BAKED ME THESE DELICIOUS *MUFFINS.*

BUT THAT'S NOT MY *JOB.* I DID IT BECAUSE I *WANTED* TO.

BUT BAKING LINGONBERRY MUFFINS IS *HARD WORK.* YOU HAD TO PICK *ALL* OF THESE LINGONBERRIES. YOU CAN'T HAVE *LINGONBERRY MUFFINS* WITHOUT *LINGONBERRIES!*

THAT'S TRUE. THOSE BRANCHES DO GET REALLY *PINCHY.*

AND YOU HAD TO MIX THE BATTER AND KEEP WATCH OVER THEM TO MAKE SURE YOU BAKED THEM JUST RIGHT.

YOU'RE *RIGHT,* I DID...

MOST IMPORTANTLY, YOU THOUGHT TO *BRING* THEM TO ME ON MY *LAST DAY* AT WORK.

I ENJOY DOING THESE THINGS...

...BUT I WANT TO DO *MORE* FOR THE PEOPLE OF ARENDELLE.

AAAAIIIIIEEEEEE--!

NYAAAAH

WHOOP!

ARE YOU *ALL* RIGHT?

I HAD THINGS *UNDER* *CONTROL.*

ARE YOU SURE ABOUT THAT?

COME ON! WE SHOULD GET TO SAFETY UNTIL THAT *DEER* IS OFF THE STREET.

IT'S A *ROEBUCK*--AND I'M NOT GOING *ANYWHERE.* NOT UNTIL I *SAVE* IT!

"*SAVE* IT"? BUT, MISS--

CALL ME *MARI.* TRUST ME. I KNOW WHAT I'M DOING. BUT I NEED YOUR HELP--

15

WHOA!

NYAAA

"GET THAT SCRUFFY-LOOKING MAN WHO SMELLS LIKE A REINDEER TO LEND YOU HIS ROPE."

KRISTOFF-- I NEED YOU TO DO SOMETHING FOR ME! PLEASE!

HI! I HAVE TO *BORROW* THIS FOR A MOMENT...

I'VE *ALWAYS* WANTED TO DO THAT!

NYAAAA

WHERE DO YOU THINK *YOU'RE* GOING, MISTER? BACK TO THE OTHER SIDE! SHOO!

SHE ACTUALLY *DID* IT! THE ROEBUCK'S HEADING TOWARD YOU!

NOW, KRISTOFF!

MAAHH

KRILLLKK

KRILKK

HOW--? WHO--?

YOU MUST BE *NEW* TO ARENDELLE.

IT'S *ALL RIGHT,* EVERYONE, YOU'RE *SAFE--*

--THE SITUATION IS UNDER CONTROL.

HER POWERS... ...I'VE HEARD STORIES--LEGENDS--BUT I THOUGHT--THEY'RE...

...MAGNIFICENT.

THAT'S MY SISTER!

BE CAREFUL, QUEEN ELSA. THIS ANIMAL'S ANGRY...

HE'S NOT ANGRY--

--HE'S SCARED.

SCARED, HUH? HMM. I THINK YOU'RE RIGHT.

ELSA, THIS IS MY NEW FRIEND--

BONG BONG

⸉GASP⸊

BONG

BONG

--MARI--

--HUH?

BONG BONG

THAT'S... ODD.

I GUESS THIS DEER'S NOT THE *ONLY* ONE WHO FRIGHTENS EASILY.

MARI RUNNING AWAY DOESN'T MAKE SENSE.

JARVO, PLEASE BRING THIS ROEBUCK SOME FOOD AND WATER, THEN RETURN IT TO THE WESTERN WOODS--

YES, QUEEN ELSA.

LATER...

"--I HAVE SOME BUSINESS TO ATTEND TO."

≯SIGH≮

WHUMP

I ASKED AROUND AND NO ONE'S SEEN MARI *ANYWHERE*. NO ONE EVEN KNOWS WHO SHE IS.

WHY DO YOU THINK SOMEONE WOULD UP AND *RUN AWAY* LIKE THAT?

I'M SURE SHE'LL TURN UP AGAIN IN THE VILLAGE AT SOME POINT.

ARE YOU *GOING* SOMEWHERE?

I'M MEETING WITH *KING JONAS* OF *VESTERLAND*.

OH? DO YOU NEED ME TO COME ALONG?

OF *COURSE* I WANT YOU TO COME ALONG!

BUT DO YOU *NEED* ME TO COME ALONG?

ANNA, WHAT'S GOTTEN INTO YOU?

ELSA, DO I HAVE... A...A SOLID... PURPOSE?

"PURPOSE"?

A REASON FOR BEING. LIKE, A JOB OR SOMETHING--

QUEEN ELSA!

JARVO?

PARDON THE INTERRUPTION, BUT THERE'S SOMETHING YOU MUST SEE! IN THE WESTERN WOODS!

OH. WELL, FIRST THING TOMORROW, WE'LL--

I'M SORRY, YOUR HIGHNESS, BUT IT CANNOT WAIT.

IS THIS ABOUT THE ANIMAL FROM THE VILLAGE?

I'M AFRAID IT'S MUCH MORE SERIOUS.

I SEE.

ANNA, I NEED YOU TO GO TO SEE KING JONAS FOR ME. WOULD YOU?

OH, OF COURSE! I'M ON MY WAY.

I CALLED THIS MEETING BECAUSE QUEEN ELSA IS A STRONG LEADER WHO HAS EARNED GREAT RESPECT.

SINCE SHE OPENED HER CASTLE GATES, SHE'S BEEN OPEN TO--NO, EAGER TO--ADDRESS THE CONCERNS OF HER NEIGHBORING KINGDOMS.

BUT SENDING A STAND-IN IN HER PLACE TO OUR MEETING IS A SLAP IN MY FACE!

"STAND-IN"?

I WANT YOU TO KNOW, SIR, THAT YOU ARE SPEAKING TO THE PRINCESS OF ARENDELLE!

BAH! ELSA HAS THE AUTHORITY. WHAT DO YOU EVEN DO?

I-- --WELL, SOMETIMES I--

I HELP QUEEN ELSA CARE FOR THE PEOPLE OF ARENDELLE. AND...AND...

...I SPREAD CHEER AND GOODWILL.

HEINZ! GET IN HERE!

22

HEINZ IS IN HIS QUARTERS, FATHER. I SENT HIM AWAY.

YOU *WHAT?* HAVE *ALL* OF YOU GONE *MAD?*

GET IN HERE!

HEY! IT'S *YOU!* I'VE BEEN LOOKING *ALL OVER* FOR YOU!

MARI, YOU *KNOW* THIS GIRL?!

OF COURSE NOT, FATHER. THAT'D BE *IMPOSSIBLE--*

FROM THE *VILLAGE...*

I DON'T KNOW HOW YOU COULD'VE FORGOTTEN. THE RUNAWAY *ROEBUCK.* THE *ICE CAGE--*

NO... PLEASE...

UM...

I TOLD HEINZ TO CALL A MEETING WITH *QUEEN ELSA*, YET I DON'T SEE *QUEEN ELSA*.

WHERE IS QUEEN ELSA?

I'M SURE QUEEN ELSA HAS A VERY GOOD REASON FOR--

THERE *IS* NO GOOD REASON FOR STANDING UP *KING JONAS* OF VESTERLAND!

BUT--BUT--BUT...SHE *DID* SEND PRINCESS ANNA IN HER PLACE!

HI. HELLO.

AN INSULT.

TELL QUEEN ELSA THAT IF I FIND ANY MORE OF ARENDELLE'S PEOPLE ON MY LAND--

--THE *CONSEQUENCES* WILL BE *DIRE!*

YOU'D BETTER GO NOW.

WAIT-- WHAT'S GOING ON HERE?

MY FATHER'S MEN SAW SOME OF ARENDELLE'S *ROYAL GUARD* IN VESTERLAND'S *WESTERN WOODS.*

THAT'S... STRANGE. BUT WHAT I MEAN IS, WHY DID YOU RUN OFF TODAY?

WHY CAN'T WE *TALK* ABOUT IT?

I--I DON'T GET OUT MUCH. MY FATHER--

WELL, IT'S *COMPLICATED.*

THAT'S *ONE* WORD FOR IT. HEH.

HE *MEANS* WELL, HE REALLY DOES...

BUT I WISH THAT HE'D LET ME *DO* THINGS SOMETIMES.

YOU NEED A *PURPOSE!*

I CAN HELP YOU *FIND* IT! WE CAN DO IT *TOGETHER!*

MEET ME IN THE VILLAGE TOMORROW--

MARI! WHERE ARE YOU?!

I-I CAN'T. I'M SORRY.

...

25

YOU WERE *RIGHT*, JARVO--

--THIS IS UNBELIEVABLE.

WHO COULD'VE *DONE* THIS, YOUR MAJESTY? *WHY?*

I DON'T KNOW...

...BUT I'M GOING TO *FIND OUT.*

VESTERLAND CASTLE, THE NEXT DAY...

TELL HER IT'S *PRINCESS ANNA* OF *ARENDELLE*. PLEASE.

I'LL TELL YOU WHAT... JUST GO AND TELL HER THAT PRINCESS ANNA IS HERE, AND IF SHE DOESN'T WANT TO SEE ME, THEN I'LL *LEAVE*. OKAY?

BLINK TWICE FOR YES.

ANNA!

UH-HUH.

31

OOH! THEY'RE JUST LIKE ANIMALS I'VE ALWAYS READ ABOUT. THEY'RE TRYING TO ASSERT *DOMINANCE* LIKE WOLVES IN THE WILD!

ARE THEY *ALWAYS* LIKE THIS?

WELL...

IT WAS EITHER THIS OR *BLACKSMITHING*. AND WORKING WITH A *HOT OVEN* IS MORE *FUN* WHEN *CHOCOLATE'S* INVOLVED.

PRINCESS ANNA?

YOU'RE NOT WHO I EXPECTED TO SEE ON MY MORNING WALK FOR KNEIPPBRØD.

ACTUALLY, I WORK HERE NOW! WE *BOTH* DO.

LET US GET THAT KNEIPPBRØD FOR YOU, FRU OLSON.

WOULD YOU LIKE THAT *SLICED?*

NO!

YOU CAN'T SLICE THAT BREAD!

BUT, BJARNE, I *WORK* HERE...

EACH LOAF HAS TO BE SLICED JUST RIGHT--EIGHT SLICES OF EQUAL THICKNESS!

OUR *REPUTATION* IS MY *NUMBER ONE* PRIORITY.

IT'S *MINE,* TOO!

BUT IT'S MY *ONLY* PRIORITY!

35

IT TOOK TWO OF US *ALL DAY YESTERDAY* TO BAKE AND DECORATE THE CAKE. WE CAN'T DO IT ALL AGAIN IN *TWO HOURS.*

BUT THERE ARE *FIVE* OF US NOW.

SIX, IF YOU COUNT--NO, WAIT, YOU WERE ALREADY COUNTING ME. KEEP GOING.

IT WOULDN'T MATTER IF THERE WERE *THIRTY* OF US...

WITH JUST *ONE* OVEN, WE CAN ONLY BAKE ONE LAYER AT A TIME.

THE *BLACKSMITH!* ANNA SAID HE HAS AN OVEN!

YES! WE CAN BRING SOME OF THE MOLDS TO THE BLACKSMITH'S SHOP AND BAKE THE CAKE IN HALF THE TIME!

HMM...I DON'T THINK HE'LL GO FOR IT.

THIS IS *ARENDELLE!* WE *HELP* EACH OTHER!

HE COULDN'T *POSSIBLY* SAY NO.

THE BLACKSMITH'S WORKSHOP.

NO.

I DON'T MEAN TO BE *RUDE*, PRINCESS ANNA, BUT...

...THE *BAKERS* AND I...WELL, WE HAVE A *HISTORY*.

I USED TO GO TO THEIR BAKERY EVERY SUNDAY FOR *POTATO DUMPLINGS*. THEIRS ARE THE *BEST*--NO OTHER BAKERY CAN MAKE THEM JUST LIKE MAMMA USED TO MAKE.

ONE SUNDAY, I WENT IN AND THEY WERE *ARGUING* ABOUT SOMETHING OR OTHER...

NOT SURPRISING...

...AND FORGOT MY DUMPLINGS IN THE OVEN A BIT TOO LONG. THEY DIDN'T TASTE THE SAME, SO I ASKED IF THEY COULD MAKE NEW ONES.

THAT'S WHEN THEY STOPPED FIGHTING WITH *EACH OTHER* AND STARTED YELLING AT *ME*. IN FRONT OF THE ENTIRE VILLAGE! THEY ACCUSED ME OF TRYING TO RUIN THEIR REPUTATION!

NO MATTER HOW MUCH I MISS MY MAMMA, I WON'T EVER GO BACK THERE AGAIN. AND I WON'T *HELP* THEM!

IS THAT *ALL* THIS IS *ABOUT*? WHAT IF THEY JUST *APOLOGIZE*?

WOULD THEY ACTUALLY *DO* THAT?

I DON'T SEE WHY NOT!

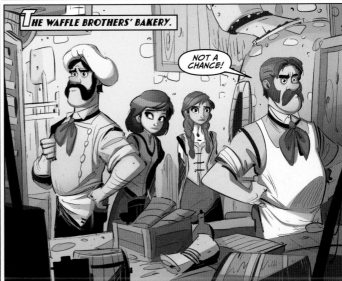

THE WAFFLE BROTHERS' BAKERY.

NOT A CHANCE!

39

40

41

LET'S SEE... HALF OFF SCARVES, SNOW SHOES...

WAGON SKIS (OF MY OWN INVENTION!) NOW IN STOCK!

AH, YES! AND A LIP BALM OF MY OWN INVENTION. ALL *HALF OFF.* IT'S--

THE *BIG WINTER BLOWOUT.*

DON'T WORRY, OAKEN, MARI AND I HAVE *GOT* THIS!

OH! DON'T FORGET ABOUT THE *FUELLERS* IN THE *SAUNA!*

YOO-HOO, FUELLERS!

YOO-HOO!

YOU HAVE TO CHECK ON THEM FROM TIME TO TIME TO MAKE SURE THEY HAVEN'T NODDED OFF.

I'M SO GRATEFUL YOU BOTH WOULD LIKE TO WORK MY TRADING POST WHILE I'M AT MY *FAMILY REUNION.*

HELP YOURSELF TO AS MUCH OF MY *CANNED MACKEREL* AS YOU LIKE!

OH! AND ONE MORE *THING...*

44

OAKEN ORDERED TWO *SAWS* AND TWO PAIRS OF *TONGS* FOR SOME CUSTOMERS. PROBLEM IS, MY NEW SHIPMENT NEVER SHOWED UP AT *PORT.*

SECOND TIME IN TWO WEEKS. CAN YOU *BELIEVE* IT?

THAT'S *UNUSUAL?*

VERY. SOMEONE'S GOT TO BE *HIJACKING* THESE SHIPS. NOW I'VE ONLY GOT *ONE* OF EACH TOOL FOR YOU.

WHY WOULD ANYONE *DO* SUCH A THING?

FINISHED!

WHY DOES *ANYONE* STEAL *ANYTHING?*

GREED.

TELL OAKEN I'M SORRY.

SIR?

OH! YOU'RE WELCOME.

SWIF

OH, YEAH. THANKS.

DING-A-LING

CLNK

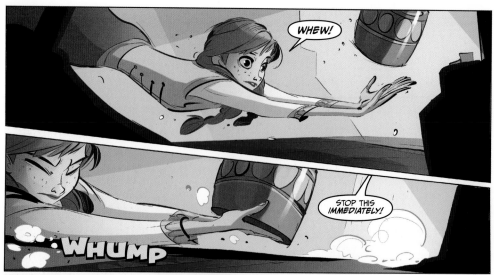

CAN'T YOU TWO BE MORE LIKE *CHIMPANZEES?*

WHEN CHIMPANZEES HUNT FOR FOOD, THEY SEND SOME OF THEIR TEAM OUT TO *CHASE* THEIR PREY--NOT TO *CATCH* THEM, BUT TO DRIVE THEM IN A CERTAIN DIRECTION...

...WHILE THE *OTHER* CHIMPANZEES WAIT IN A TREE FOR THE PERFECT OPPORTUNITY TO DROP DOWN AND *TRAP* THEM.

WHAT ARE YOU *TALKING* ABOUT?

WHY DOESN'T *ONE* OF YOU *CUT* THE ICE WITH THE *SAW*--

--AND THE *OTHER* SCOOP UP THE ICE WITH THE *TONGS?*

IF YOU'RE EACH CONCENTRATING ON JUST *ONE JOB,* YOU CAN WORK TWICE AS FAST AND PRODUCE *MORE* THAN ENOUGH FOR THE *BOTH* OF YOU.

LIKE CHIMPANZEES.

THAT SOUNDS ALL RIGHT TO ME. HOW ABOUT YOU?

ME TOO. I'M SORRY THAT I TRIED TO RUN OFF WITH THE TOOLS. I GUESS I LOST MY HEAD.

I GUESS THAT SETTLES IT, THEN.

THANK YOU, MISS. MY FAMILY'S VERY GRATEFUL!

WHAT'S A CHIMPANZEE?

WAIT...

...DON'T SLAM THAT--

SLAM

KRSH

--DOOR.

HEINZ!

RIGHT HERE, YOUR MAJESTY.

ARE YOU CERTAIN THE PROPER ARRANGEMENTS HAVE BEEN MADE?

YES, YOUR MAJESTY. QUEEN ELSA IS WAITING FOR YOU NOW. NO *STAND-INS* THIS TIME.

HEINZ!

STILL HERE, YOUR MAGNIFICENCE.

AND THE CONSTRUCTION?

AHEAD OF SCHEDULE, YOUR GRACIOUSNESS.

SOON YOU WILL HAVE THE LARGEST CASTLE IN THE REALM.

YOUR HIGHNESS!

WE FOUND *THIS* IN PRINCESS MARI'S ROOM! SHE'S *GONE!*

NOT AGAIN!

HEINZ!

UHHHUHH...

CANCEL THE MEETING!

BUT KING JONAS! QUEEN ELSA--THE *TRESPASSERS* ON YOUR *LAND*--

THAT WILL HAVE TO *WAIT* UNTIL MY DAUGHTER IS BACK IN THE CASTLE, SAFE AND SOUND!

I WILL *NOT* LOSE HER LIKE I LOST MY *KARINA!*

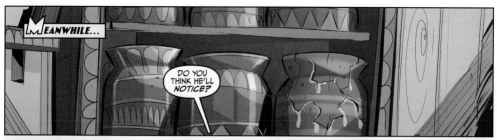

DO YOU THINK HE'LL *NOTICE?*

THIS GLUE OAKEN INVENTED IS *AMAZING...*

...BUT NOT *THAT* AMAZING.

≹SIGH≸ IT'S NOT LIKE WE WOULD *KEEP* IT FROM HIM ANYWAY--AND OAKEN'S AN UNDERSTANDING PERSON. BUT STILL...

...I HATE TO HAVE TO CLOSE THE STORE WITH NOTHING TO SHOW FOR IT BUT A BROKEN POT.

WE DID *GREAT* TODAY, WE CAN'T LET IT END LIKE THIS.

MAYBE THE TRADING POST ISN'T WHAT WE WERE MEANT TO DO EITHER.

I WANT TO DO SOMETHING MORE *IMPORTANT.* I WANT TO BE OUT IN THE *WORLD.*

LIKE *THEM.* THE *ICE HARVESTERS.*

THE NORTH MOUNTAIN.

EVENING.

REST UP WHILE YOU CAN, SVEN. THE RIDE BACK'LL BE MUCH HEAVIER THAN THE RIDE IN.

HI, KRISTOFF!

YOU REMEMBER MARI.

ANNA? WHAT ARE YOU DOING HERE? WHERE'D YOU GET THE SLED?

IT'S A RENTAL. AND WHY DO YOU THINK WE'RE HERE?

WE'RE GONNA HARVEST ICE!

SINCE WHEN DO YOU WANT TO DO THAT? IT'S HARD WORK.

NOT THAT YOU CAN'T DO HARD WORK. WHAT I MEAN IS, YOU HAVE TO BE PROPERLY TRAINED AND KNOW HOW TO WORK IN SYNC WITH THE OTHERS.

THESE GUYS WON'T WANT TO GIVE A SPOT TO A COUPLE OF FIRST-TIMERS.

WE KNOW THAT.

YOU DO?

THAT'S WHY WE BROUGHT *SANDWICHES!*

SOMEONE SAY SANDWICHES?

I COULD EAT!

HEY, GUYS! THESE NEWBIES BROUGHT *SANDWICHES!*

FRIENDS OF YOURS, KRISTOFF?

THOSE TWO? WHAT'RE *THEY* DOING HERE?

AHEM. SOMETHING *WRONG,* LARS?

HM? NAH. EVERYTHING'S... FINE.

BUT HOW ARE YOU GOING TO DO THE JOB IF YOU DON'T HAVE THE *TOOLS?*

THEY CAN BORROW MINE!

KRAKKT

HUH--?

KRAKKT

WHAT? NYAAAAAAAA!

MARI?!

M-MARI?!

PART THREE

DON'T MESS WITH US

WHA--?

SPLISH

WHEW.

YEAH! YAHOO!

I TOLD YOU ICE HARVESTING WAS *DANGEROUS* WORK.

WHEN HAS *THAT* EVER STOPPED ME BEFORE?

ARE YOU TWO *ALL RIGHT?*

I DON'T KNOW WHAT HAPPENED--THE ICE JUST *BROKE.* BUT WE WON'T LET THAT *STOP* US! PROMISE!

LET'S LEAVE THE REST OF THE CUTTING TO THE *OTHERS...*

I'VE BEEN LOOKING FOR A RESOURCEFUL PAIR OF NEW HARVESTERS LIKE YOU FOR ANOTHER *SPECIFIC* TASK.

LARS! DON'T GO ANYWHERE JUST YET!

THERE'S BEEN A CHANGE OF PLANS. YOU'RE GOING TO *WESELTON* NOW AND ANNA AND MARI ARE ON *SHIPYARD* DETAIL.

BUT THAT'S *MY* ROUTE! I JUST LOADED *THIS* SLED WITH THE ICE ORDER FOR THE *SHIPYARD*.

AND NOW YOU CAN LOAD THEIR *RENTAL* WITH THE ICE ORDER FOR *WESELTON*. UNLESS...

...THERE'S *SOME OTHER* REASON YOU WON'T SURRENDER THE KEY TO THE SHIPYARD...

BOATS HAVE BEEN GOING MISSING LATELY. THE SHIPYARD COULD BE *DANGEROUS*. BUT IF YOU INSIST...

AFTER WHAT I JUST SAW THESE TWO DO, THEY'RE *MORE* THAN CAPABLE OF TAKING CARE OF THEMSELVES.

ALL RIGHT, SVEN--LET'S LOAD UP AND--

NYAAAA!

WHOA! WHAT'S THE MATTER, BUDDY?

WHO, LARS? HE'S JUST TRYING TO SCARE THEM.

ROOOO!

ALL RIGHT, ALL RIGHT! PUT YOUR *REINDEER BREATH* AWAY!

BYE, KRISTOFF! BYE, SVEN!

RRFF!

FINE. IF YOU REALLY THINK THE SHIPYARD IS *DANGEROUS*, WE'LL FOLLOW THEM.

BUT WE'D BETTER GO AROUND THE *OTHER* SIDE OF THE MOUNTAIN, 'CAUSE IF ANNA THINKS WE'RE NOT CONFIDENT SHE CAN TAKE CARE OF HERSELF--

VESTERLAND CASTLE.

"--SHE'LL NEVER SPEAK TO US AGAIN!"

WHAT DO YOU *MEAN* YOU STILL HAVEN'T FOUND HER?! I WILL HAVE ALL YOUR HEADS FOR THIS!

D-DON'T WORRY, YOUR MAJESTY. WE'RE TAKING OUR SEARCH *OUTSIDE* THE CASTLE WALLS. WE--WE'VE GOT *SOME IDEA* OF WHERE SHE MIGHT BE.

ANY IDEA WHERE SHE MIGHT BE?

SHE'LL RETURN HOME, ADAM--SHE *ALWAYS* DOES...

MY CONCERN RIGHT NOW IS THIS BUSINESS WITH ARENDELLE.

THE KING MUST SIT DOWN WITH QUEEN ELSA TO FIND OUT WHY HER GUARDS WERE TRESPASSING ON OUR LAND...

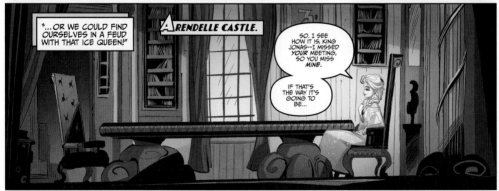

"...OR WE COULD FIND OURSELVES IN A FEUD WITH THAT ICE QUEEN!"

ARENDELLE CASTLE.

SO, I SEE HOW IT IS, KING JONAS--I MISSED *YOUR* MEETING, SO YOU MISS *MINE.*

IF THAT'S THE WAY IT'S GOING TO BE...

...A NEW PEACE IS GOING TO BE HARDER TO ACHIEVE THAN I THOUGHT.

HOLY *MACKEREL*, THAT'S A LOT OF MACKEREL!

THEY'RE *HADDOCK. MELANOGRAMMUS AEGLEFINUS.* YOU CAN TELL BY THE DARK SMUDGE ON THEIR SIDES.

POOR CREATURES CAME TO THE FJORD TO *SPAWN* AND INSTEAD ENDED UP ON ICE.

SO WE'RE NOT THE *ONLY* ONES WHO'VE HAD A ROUGH DAY.

PSST! HEY--IS THAT *YOU?*

HEY! YOU'RE NOT LARS--

LARS? YOU *KNOW* LARS?

THAT WE *DO*, LADY, AND THAT'S *OUR KEY!*

YEAH, *OUR* KEY!

YOUR KEY?

TELL US WHAT YOU DID WITH HIM, OR WE'LL--

STOP RIGHT THERE, YOU TWO!

YOU SHOULD ALREADY *KNOW* WHAT THESE TWO ARE ABOUT TO *LEARN*--

NO ONE GETS ONE OVER ON OLD LARS!

⸗GASP⸗

63

EASY, SVEN!

I KNOW WE LIKE TO GO *FAST*, BUT I SWALLOWED TWO BUGS AND MY CLOTHES ARE TURNING INSIDE OUT--

YOU THERE! HALT!

BY THE ORDER OF KING JONAS OF *VESTERLAND!*

VESTERLAND? THIS IS... THIS IS *ARENDELLE!*

ISN'T IT?

TURN THIS WAGON AROUND AT ONCE.

MY REINDEER'S IN KIND OF A *HURRY*, SO IF YOU'D JUST LET ME PASS--

AT ONCE! UNLESS YOU *AND* YOUR REINDEER ARE EAGER TO SEE THE INSIDE OF OUR *DUNGEON...*

OKAY, OKAY, KEEP YOUR *HAT* ON. I'M *GOING.* SHEESH.

BUT SOMETHING *STRANGE* IS GOING ON HERE.

ROOOO?

NO, SVEN...

"...I *DON'T* KNOW WHERE THE ANIMALS HAVE GONE."

IT'S NOT *THEIR* FAULT, JARVO--THEY'VE BEEN DRIVEN FROM THEIR HOMES WITH NOWHERE ELSE TO GO.

WE'VE REACHED OUT TO THE KING OF VESTERLAND, QUEEN ELSA, BUT THERE'S BEEN NO RESPONSE.

WHAT'S OUR NEXT MOVE?

WE WAIT *LONGER.*

ARENDELLE'S BEEN PEACEFUL FOR *CENTURIES.* I'M NOT GOING TO DO ANYTHING THAT VESTERLAND MIGHT TAKE AS A HOSTILE ACT.

I JUST WISH *ANNA* WERE HERE. SHE'S BEEN OUT SOMEWHERE ALL DAY... SHE'D KNOW HOW TO BRING OUR KINGDOMS TOGETHER.

DON'T WORRY ABOUT PRINCESS ANNA--

"--SHE KNOWS HOW TO HANDLE HERSELF."

YOU'LL BE *SORRY!* MY SISTER'S QUEEN ELSA OF ARENDELLE! SHE'LL HAVE YOU *JAILED* WHEN SHE FINDS OUT YOU'RE THE ONES HIJACKING THE SHIPS!

YOU? A *PRINCESS?* HAULING ICE TO THE SHIPYARD?

YOU'LL HAVE TO COME UP WITH BETTER THAN *THAT ONE* TO FOOL ME!

WE CAN'T LET THEM GET AWAY!

OH! I KNOW!

≈NYAHH≈ HEY, LEIF! YEAH, *YOU!* LOOK AT *ME!* ≈RRRR≈

YOU NAMED THE REINDEER "LEIF"?

≈HAWWW≈ I'M *ANOTHER* BIG, BAD *REINDEER* COMING INTO *YOUR* TERRITORY! ≈WROOO!≈

MARI... WHAT ARE YOU *DOING?!*

GOOD BOY, LEIF!

SLIKT

66

MARI, THAT WAS--WELL, STRANGE--BUT AMAZING!

IF WE HURRY, WE CAN STILL CATCH LARS' SHIP!

HOW ARE WE GOING TO DO THAT? WE DON'T HAVE A BOAT!

DON'T WE?

FASTER, LEIF, FASTER!

GO, BOY, GO!

MARI--

--NOW!

KRAKT

DON'T BE AFRAID OF THE WATER, MARI--WE MADE IT!

STOLEN SHIP, DEAD AHEAD!

AROOOOOOOO!

SPLRRSH

Soon...

--SO IT TURNS OUT THAT *LARS* AND HIS *CRONIES* WERE THE ONES WHO'VE BEEN HIJACKING THE SHIPS--AND WE PUT A *STOP* TO IT!

ANNA, THAT'S *INCREDIBLE!*

ALL IN A DAY'S WORK. EH, MARI?

MARI? WHAT'S WRONG?

ALL OF IT.

THE CAKE AT THE BAKERY WAS RUINED BECAUSE OF US--

--WE ALMOST DESTROYED WANDERING OAKEN'S--

--WE EVEN GAVE LARS HIS OWN KEY TO THE SHIPYARD AND ALMOST HAD A BOAT STOLEN RIGHT OUT FROM UNDER OUR NOSES!

IT WAS JUST OUR *FIRST DAY.* WE'LL FIND *SOMETHING* THAT--

NO. I'M *DONE.* THIS-- THIS WAS A *MISTAKE.*

I HAVE TO FACE IT, ANNA--

--I'M NOT MEANT TO BE ANYTHING BUT KING JONAS'S DAUGHTER.

MARI! WAIT--

LET HER GO, ANNA--YOU CAN CHECK IN ON HER LATER. WE'VE GOT TO GET LARS TO THE AUTHORITIES. WHICH REMINDS ME--

--SOMETHING *STRANGE* HAPPENED IN ARENDELLE ON MY WAY OVER HERE...

73

ELSA? *ELSA?*

SHE'S PROBABLY ALREADY MEETING WITH JARVO ABOUT THIS!

ELS--

YOUNG LADY, WHAT DO YOU THINK YOU'RE DOING?

I'M LOOKING FOR MY *FATH--*

OH!

≥HUFF≤ SORRY, PRINCESS ANNA ≥HUFF≤ BUT THE GUARDS ARE ALL ≥HUFF≤ AT THE WESTERN TOWERS ≥HUFF≤...

IT'S ALL RIGHT, GERDA. MARI'S MY *FRIEND.* YOU CAN LEAVE US.

I THOUGHT YOU WERE GOING *HOME.*

I *DID.* NO ONE WAS THERE. I THOUGHT-- I *HOPED*--FATHER WAS HERE.

ME *TOO*--SO I COULD FIND OUT WHY *VESTERLAND GUARDS* ARE ASSEMBLING IN *ARENDELLE.*

GUARDS? SO I'M *TOO LATE?*

74

YOU *KNEW* THIS WOULD HAPPEN?

YES--ER, *NO*-- I...I WAS HOPING TO *STOP* HIM FROM RETALIATING FOR ARENDELLE'S GUARDS TRESPASSING IN VESTERLAND'S WESTERN WOODS...

BUT THE WESTERN WOODS ARE IN ARENDELLE.

ELSA DECLARED THAT AREA OFF-LIMITS TO HUNTERS AND BUILDERS. OUR GUARDS ARE ONLY THERE TO MAKE SURE IT STAYS THAT WAY.

IT'S OUR *ANIMAL SANCTUARY.*

SEE?

BUT ACCORDING TO *OUR* MAPS... THAT'S VESTERLAND TERRITORY!

"WE HAVE TO TELL ELSA RIGHT AWAY!"

IS THIS WHAT YOU'VE BEEN DOING FOR THE PAST DAY AND NIGHT?

THAT'S A WHOLE *OTHER* STORY...

BUT MARI SAYS SHE'LL JUST ASK KING JONAS TO STOP BUILDING SO THE SANCTUARY CAN STAY.

DO YOU REALLY THINK KING JONAS WOULD *AGREE* TO THAT?

OF COURSE! HE KNOWS HOW MUCH I LOVE *ANIMALS...*

LATER AT YESTERLAND CASTLE.

"...AND HE'D DO *ANYTHING* FOR *ME!*"

MARI! MY DEAR, SWEET *MARI!*

I WAS SO AFRAID I'D *LOST* YOU LIKE I'D LOST YOUR *MOTHER!*

TELL ME-- WHAT DID THEY *DO* TO YOU?! DID THEY *HURT* YOU?

NO, NOT *AT ALL*, FATHER! PRINCESS ANNA'S MY *FRIEND.*

SHE SHOWED ME SOMETHING YOU WON'T *BELIEVE*--WE HAVE TO STOP THE CONSTRUCTION IN THE WESTERN WOODS *RIGHT AWAY!*

ABSOLUTELY *NOT!*

BUT, *FATHER*, IT SAYS HERE IN THIS *BOOK* THAT THE LAND ACTUALLY BELONGS TO *ARENDELLE*-- IT'S AN *ANIMAL SANCTUARY.*

HOW *CONVENIENT*. *THEIR* BOOK!

I'M BUILDING THE CASTLE'S EXTENSION FOR *YOU!*

FOR *ME?!*

MARI AND I WERE OUT ALL DAY LOOKING FOR *JOBS* TO DO BECAUSE WE FELT WE NEEDED A *PURPOSE*. I GUESS WE WANTED TO FEEL MORE USEFUL.

BUT WE RAN INTO PROBLEMS EVERYWHERE WE WENT. AND MARI WAS ABLE TO SOLVE *EVERY ONE* OF THEM WITH HER KNOWLEDGE OF ANIMALS.

SHE'S *DIFFERENT* FROM ANYONE I'VE EVER MET--AND THAT'S PART OF WHAT MAKES HER *SPECIAL*.

SHE'D BE A *GREAT* AMBASSADOR!

WITH MARI AS AMBASSADOR, ARENDELLE IS WILLING TO *SHARE* THE WESTERN WOODS WITH VESTERLAND--BUT *ONLY* IF IT REMAINS AN ANIMAL SANCTUARY.

AND MARI WOULD STILL BE ABLE TO WORK WITH *ANNA*-- ARENDELLE'S *NATURAL* AMBASSADOR.

I *AM?*

OF COURSE. YOUR COMPASSION AND FRIENDLINESS ARE GREAT ASSETS TO OUR KINGDOM.

YOU DIDN'T HAVE TO GO OUT TO LOOK FOR YOUR PURPOSE, IT WAS RIGHT HERE ALL ALONG.

SO WHAT DO YOU SAY, KING JONAS?

VESTERLAND HASN'T HAD AN AMBASSADOR TO ARENDELLE SINCE BEFORE YOU CLOSED THE CASTLE GATES...

AND MAYBE THAT'S BEEN OUR PROBLEM.

YES. I SAY YES.

"COME...

"...LET'S COAX THE ANIMALS BACK TO THEIR LAND...

"...AND THEN WE'LL CELEBRATE OUR RENEWED FRIENDSHIP THANKS TO OUR *EXTRAORDINARY* PRINCESSES--ANNA AND MY MARI!"

THE END.

DISNEP

FROZEN

REUNION ROAD

ARENDELLE.

PART ONE
BRIDGING THE DIVIDE

ELSA! ELSA!

IT'S A LETTER FOR QUEEN ELSA-- WHOOP!

SLOOSH

SPLOSH

SPLOSH SPLOSH

SPLOSH

OLAF?

THIS CAME FOR YOU...

YOU COULD SAY, I...

...WELL, I KNOW A BIT-- BUT IT'S BEEN A LONG...

KAI... ARE YOU *ALL* RIGHT?

WELL, I GUESS...I SORT OF--

OOH! HAVE YOU *BEEN* THERE? TELL US EVERYTHING YOU KNOW!

WELL...I WAS...

...I WAS *BORN* THERE.

KAI! YOU'RE *FROM* SNOOB?! HOW COME WE'VE NEVER HEARD THIS?

IT'S A SENSITIVE SUBJECT, QUEEN ELSA. IT--IT'S MY *BROTHER.*

YOU HAVE *FAMILY* THERE?

THAT SETTLES IT--WE'RE *GOING* TO THAT HARVEST FESTIVAL AND *YOU'RE* COMING WITH US.

I HAVEN'T SPOKEN TO KARL IN *YEARS*--WE LOST CONTACT AFTER KING AGNARR CLOSED THE CASTLE GATES.

IT MAY BE TOO UNCOMFORTABLE...

BEING APART FOR SO LONG MIGHT HAVE MADE YOUR BOND EVEN *STRONGER.* RIGHT ELSA?

YOU *HAVE* TO REUNITE WITH KARL, KAI.

BAH, IT'S A NONISSUE, ANYWAY. I'M SURE HE'S FORGOTTEN ALL ABOUT ME.

FAMILY DOESN'T FORGET ABOUT FAMILY JUST BECAUSE YOU'RE *APART*, KAI.

SEE?

SO...

"...WE'RE *ALL* GOING TO SNOOB *TOGETHER!*"

DON'T YOU WORRY, QUEEN ELSA, EVERYTHING WILL BE IN ORDER WHILE YOU'RE AWAY.

I TRUST IT *WILL*, GERDA. WE CAN ALWAYS COUNT ON YOU.

BRING ME BACK SOMETHING SNOOBISH! A HONEY BUZZARD...OR A BARNACLE GOOSE...

I'LL...SEE WHAT I CAN DO, MARI!

IS THE *WAGON* READY?

IT'S *PACKED*, WAXED...

...AND READY FOR AN *ADVENTURE!*

THEN LET'S GO!

FIRST THINGS FIRST, PRINCESS ANNA...

FROM WHAT I REMEMBER, SNOOB IS BIG ON *TRADITIONS*. IT IS CUSTOMARY FOR GUESTS TO RETURN THE FAVOR OF AN INVITATION...

"...BY BRINGING GIFTS."

HOO-HOO! IF YOU'RE LOOKING FOR SOMETHING PRACTICAL, I'VE GOT JUST THE THING FOR YOU!

THESE CLIPPERS OF MY OWN INVENTION ARE PERFECT FOR TRIMMING A MUSTACHE--OR YOUR TOENAILS.

PEOPLE TRIM THEIR TOENAILS?

OR PERHAPS YOUR FRIENDS WOULD ENJOY A GIFT CERTIFICATE TO OAKEN'S SAUNA?

SVEN, BE HONEST--DOES THIS HAT MAKE MY NOSE LOOK BIG?

YEAH, YOU'RE RIGHT. IT DOESN'T MAKE IT LOOK ⨟HRN⨟ BIG ENOUGH--

BOY, THAT'S REALLY STUCK ON THERE, ISN'T IT?

I WAS THINKING MAYBE SOMETHING MORE *TRADITIONAL*, OAKEN. *SYMBOLIC*. LIKE THAT *BUKKEHORN* RIGHT THERE.

A *SHEPHERD'S CALL HORN* IS A *SPLENDID* CHOICE FOR A HARVEST FESTIVAL, QUEEN ELSA! AND VERY *SNOOBISH*.

I LOVE BUKKEHORNS, BUT I WANT SOMETHING THEY'VE NEVER SEEN BEFORE.

LET ME THINK...

THERE IT IS!

POP

HUH?!

WHAT DO YOU HAVE THAT THE **WHOLE FAMILY** CAN ENJOY? SOMETHING THAT WILL BRING EVERYONE **TOGETHER.**

A **LOCAL DELICACY** IS ALWAYS A CROWD PLEASER--

--WOULD YOU LIKE THE DRIED **SMALAHOVE?** OR A CAN OF **FISKBOLLER?**

GREAT-- NOW MY MOUTH IS WATERING.

ACTUALLY... I WAS THINKING SOMETHING MORE LIKE...

...LIKE **THIS** OVER HERE.

ERR... WHAT **IS** THAT?

AN INVENTION OF MY **BROTHER'S.** IT'S USED TO CLIP YOUR PAPERS TOGETHER SO THEY DON'T BLOW AWAY.

YOUR **BROTHER** IS AN INVENTOR, TOO?

OH, YES! I COME FROM A **WHOLE FAMILY** OF INVENTORS...

SAFE TRAVELS!

ACCORDING TO THE MAP, WE START OUT DUE EAST, THEN HEAD SOUTH AT--

EAST? GOING ALL THE WAY AROUND WILL TAKE *FOREVER.* WE'LL GO *SOUTH.*

THEN HOW WILL WE CROSS *GUFEN GORGE?*

THAT MUST BE AN *OLD* MAP. THERE'S A *BRIDGE* NOT TOO FAR FROM HERE THAT GOES ACROSS.

GRANTED IT'S BEEN A WHILE, BUT I RECALL TRAVELING THROUGH THE *VALLEY...*

IT *IS* AN OLD MAP, BUT... KRISTOFF, ARE YOU *SURE?*

IF WE WANT AS MUCH TIME AS POSSIBLE TO SPEND *AT THE FESTIVAL,* THE BRIDGE IS THE FASTEST WAY.

BRIDGE

"TRUST ME."

DANGER BRIDGE CLOSED

SLOOSH

SOUTH...EAST... IT DOESN'T MATTER, THEY *BOTH* SOUND FUN TO ME!

AND--*HEY!* LET'S SING SOME *TRAVEL* SONGS!

I WROTE ONE JUST FOR THIS SPECIAL OCCASION. WANNA HEAR IT?

OF COURSE!

OH BOY.

WHEN WE FINALLY GET TO SNOOB... OH, THE THINGS I'M GONNA DOOB...

REALLY?

PLUCK ON THE STRINGS TO MAKE BEAUTIFUL MUSIC...

NO, OLAF, IT'S A HARVEST FESTIVAL, NOT A HARPIST FESTIVAL--

LA LA LA LA LA LA LA LA LA LA LA LA-- CREEEAAAK

DOES ANYONE ELSE *HEAR* THAT?

I'M NOT SURE I CAN *UNHEAR* IT.

NO... IT'S...

WHUNK THUNK

UHN!

WHERE DID THEY GO? WHERE'S *ANNA?* AND *SVEN?*

ANNA?

KAI? OLAF?

ANYBODY? CAN YOU *HEAR* ME?

ANNA?!

PART TWO

HER SPECIAL GIFT

KRISTOFF? WHEN THE BRIDGE COLLAPSED, ANNA, KAI, SVEN, AND OLAF SLID DOWN *THAT* SIDE OF THE *GORGE.*

I KNOW.

THEN SHOULDN'T WE GO *THAT* WAY?

ANNA AND I ONCE MADE A *DEAL* WHILE *HIKING*. IF WE'RE EVER SEPARATED, WE AGREED TO CONTINUE ON TO THE DESTINATION SO WE DON'T WASTE TIME WALKING IN CIRCLES LOOKING FOR EACH OTHER.

LEAVE IT TO ANNA TO COME UP WITH A PLAN AS PRACTICAL AS THAT.

NOT TO BRAG, BUT IT WAS ACTUALLY *MY* IDEA.

BUT WHAT IF THEY'RE *HURT*... OR *WORSE?*

WE CAN'T THINK LIKE THAT, ELSA. WE BOTH KNOW THAT ANNA CAN HANDLE HERSELF.

BESIDES, *SVEN* IS WITH THEM. HE KNOWS THE LAND AS WELL AS I DO.

NOW LET'S SEE...IF THAT WAY IS *NORTH,* THEN SNOOB IS...

HA HA!

YOU'RE *LOST,* AREN'T YOU?

ELSA?

ELLL-SSSSSAAAAAAAA!

QUEEN ELSA! ARE YOU OUT THERE?

COME ON, SVEN--NOW THAT I'VE GOT MY *BOTTOM* BACK, LET'S RIDE THE ICE SLIDE AGAIN!

SORRY, OLAF. THAT WAS A *ONE-WAY* TRIP AND WE'VE GOT A *HARVEST FESTIVAL* TO GET TO!

BUT PRINCESS ANNA...MAYBE WE SHOULD FIND OUR WAY BACK TO *ARENDELLE* AND HAVE THE GUARDS HELP WITH THE SEARCH...

ONE TIME, KRISTOFF AND I GOT SEPARATED ON A HIKE AND CIRCLED FOR *HOURS* TO LOOK FOR EACH OTHER, WHEN I COULD'VE FOUND HIM IN *MINUTES* HAD I KEPT GOING.

I DECIDED THAT IF WE EVER GOT SEPARATED *AGAIN*, THAT'S WHAT WE'D DO--KEEP MOVING TOWARD OUR DESTINATION.

I KNOW KRISTOFF AND ELSA ARE SAFELY ON THEIR WAY TO SNOOB JUST LIKE WE ARE.

WE'RE GOING TO THAT *HARVEST FESTIVAL* AND I *WILL* REUNITE YOU WITH YOUR LONG LOST BROTHER...

...EVEN IF WE HAVE TO RIDE ALL THE WAY THERE ON *SVEN'S BACK!*

HROO?

SEE? I TOLD YOU I FOUND--

--WHA...?

WELL *THIS* IS A MAJOR LETDOWN.

HEY, WATCH IT--

--THAT'S MY *FAMILY.*

BRUNA! WHEN DID YOU SNEAK AWAY?

AND WHO ARE YOUR *FRIENDS?*

THEY'RE *LOST.*

NOT LOST!

THIS IS QUEEN ELSA! AND HER *ROYAL* SERVANT!

FRIEND!

107

111

KAI! A WAGON! I BET WE CAN STILL *CATCH* UP TO IT IF WE HURRY!

SVEN! OLAF! LET'S--

O-OLAF?

OLAF, WHERE DID YOU GO?

SNF SNF

SNF

HRAAAWWW!

YOU DON'T THINK...

WE NEED A WAGON *RIGHT* AWAY!

I ACTUALLY *HAVE* ONE YOU CAN USE--

"--BUT THERE'S ONE PROBLEM..."

I NEVER THOUGHT TO GET A NEW LINCHPIN FOR THIS OLD WAGON 'CAUSE I HAVEN'T NEEDED IT IN *YEARS*. WE'RE SELF-SUFFICIENT HERE--WE RARELY HAVE TO TRAVEL OUTSIDE CITY LIMITS.

IF YOU HAPPEN TO HAVE A LINCHPIN TO FASTEN THE WHEEL TO THE HUB, THE WAGON'S YOURS TO KEEP.

WHY WOULD WE BE CARRYING A *LINCHPIN?*

BUT WE *ARE*...

HERE-- WOULD *THIS* WORK?!

𝒮HORTLY...

THAT'LL ACTUALLY *DO!* THAT'LL DO *VERY WELL!*

THANK YOU SO MUCH!

KAI, LET'S HURRY!

BUT IT'S NOT A *PERFECT* FIT. BE CAREFUL ON YOUR TURNS AND--

--DON'T GO TOO...

...FAST.

BUT I BET THERE'S AN EVEN *BIGGER* AUDIENCE IN SNOOB, RIGHT?

THE HORSES ARE DUE FOR A *REST*, ANYWAY-- WHY NOT TAKE *ADVANTAGE* OF THE CROWD? WE CAN'T BE *TOO READY* FOR THE BIG STAGE IN SNOOB.

YES. OF--OF COURSE.

YOU'D BETTER GET GOING, TOO. THE BAND IS GONNA NEED ITS *TUBA PLAYER.*

HA! WHAT?

BRUNA IS *NOT* OUR TUBA PLAYER.

BUT YOU SAID--

I *AM* A TUBA PLAYER! I MEAN...

...I *KNOW* I *COULD BE* THE *BEST* TUBA PLAYER...

...IF I WERE ONLY BIG ENOUGH TO ACTUALLY *HOLD* A TUBA.

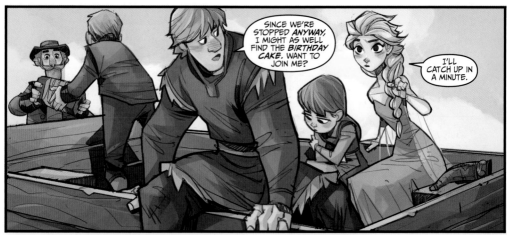

SINCE WE'RE STOPPED *ANYWAY,* I MIGHT AS WELL FIND THE *BIRTHDAY CAKE.* WANT TO JOIN ME?

I'LL CATCH UP IN A MINUTE.

BRUNA, ARE YOU OKAY?

QUEEN ELSA, DO YOU EVER FEEL--

AW, OF COURSE NOT. YOU'RE A *QUEEN.*

TRY ME. YOU'D BE SURPRISED.

IT'S JUST THAT...EVERYONE ELSE IS IN THE *BAND...*

YOU FEEL LIKE YOU DON'T BELONG.

LIKE...I'M *WITH* THEM, BUT I'M...

ISOLATED.

HOW DO YOU KNOW?

I SPENT MANY YEARS LOCKED AWAY FROM MY *FAMILY*--FROM MY SISTER--IN MY *OWN CASTLE* FOR FEAR THAT MY...SPECIAL GIFT...MIGHT DO THEM *HARM...*

--BUT ONCE EVERYONE KNEW WHAT I COULD DO, I LET GO OF MY FEAR AND GOT MY SISTER BACK. NOW, I DON'T KNOW HOW I WAS EVER ABLE TO LIVE *WITHOUT* ANNA.

LADIES AND GENTLEMAN--

119

IS THAT A *REAL* CARROT?

IT'S MY *NOSE.*

I NEVER KNEW THAT SNOWMEN COULD *TALK!*

... OLAF?

YAY! ENCORE!

BRUNA, YOU DID IT!

THAT'S MY FRIEND!

121

THE OTHER WAGON'S TRACKS LED RIGHT INTO THESE WOODS, BUT THEY'RE HARD TO MAKE OUT IN THE DARKNESS.

WE SURVIVED A *BRIDGE COLLAPSE*, A LONG *UPHILL* JOURNEY, A BROKEN WAGON WHEEL...BUT NOW I'VE LOST *OLAF*.

DON'T BLAME YOURSELF, PRINCESS ANNA. WE'LL FIND HIM.

PART THREE

It Was Worth It

AWROOOOO!

WHA--?

IT'S OKAY, IT'S JUST A *CUB.* I THINK IT MIGHT BE *HURT.*

PRINCESS ANNA, PLEASE BE CAREFUL.

WHERE THERE'S A CUB, THERE'S A *MOTHER.*

IF I'M *ABLE* TO HELP, THEN I *SHOULD.* A GOOD DEED IS *ALWAYS* WORTH THE EFFORT. DON'T YOU THINK?

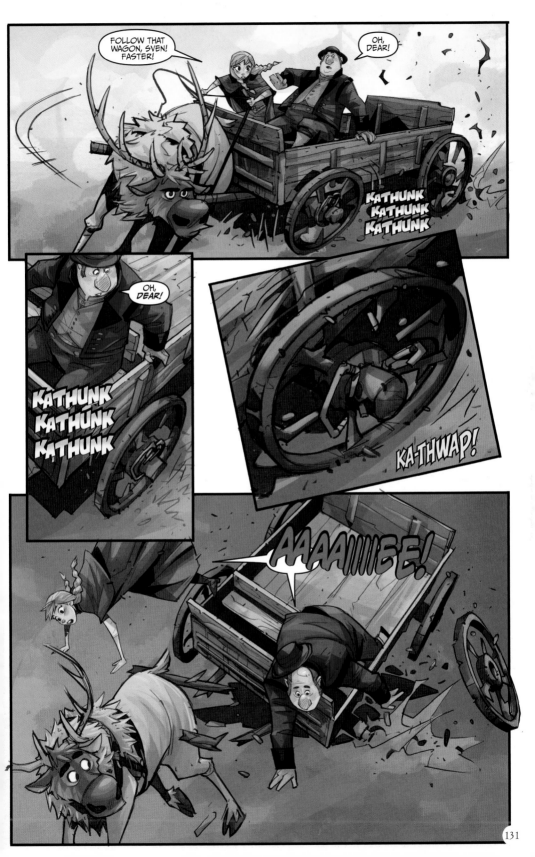

WE'RE NOT IN SNOOB *YET,* OLAF, BUT THIS NEW WAGON OF YOURS SHOULD SUIT US FINE.

EXCEPT IT BELONGS TO *SOMEONE ELSE.* SEEMS WE'RE RIGHT BACK WHERE WE STARTED-- *STRANDED.*

NOT TO MENTION *LOST.*

I THINK WE CAN ALL AGREE THAT THIS TRIP HAS BEEN DIFFICULT FROM THE START. PERHAPS WE SHOULD TAKE THIS WAGON BACK TO ITS RIGHTFUL OWNERS AND ARRANGE FOR A RIDE *HOME.*

HOME? AS IN *ARENDELLE?!*

ELSA AND I KNOW WHAT IT WAS LIKE WHEN *WE* WERE APART. WE CAN'T LET YOU BE AWAY FROM *YOUR* BROTHER ANYMORE.

MAYBE WE CAN TRY SOME OTHER TIME. AT SOME POINT, IT'S JUST NOT WORTH--

VROO OOO OO!

WHAT IN THE WORLD--?

PRINCESS ANNA, NO ONE HAS *EVER* GONE THROUGH SO MUCH TO DO SOMETHING SO NICE FOR ME BEFORE. I COULD *NEVER* REPAY YOU FOR REUNITING ME WITH KARL.

IT'S THE *LEAST* WE COULD DO AFTER ALL YOU'VE DONE FOR ELSA AND ME OVER THE YEARS. BUT I ALSO HAVE A *SURPRISE* FOR YOU...

ELSA HAS MADE ARRANGEMENTS WITH THE BARON FOR YOU TO STAY WITH KARL HERE IN SNOOB FOR A WHILE!

OH! THAT IS...VERY *NICE* OF HER...

...BUT THAT JUST NOW? THAT WAS KARL AND I SAYING OUR *GOODBYES.* IF IT'S ALL RIGHT...I'D RATHER RETURN WITH YOU TO ARENDELLE *THIS EVENING.*

AFTER ALL YOU'VE BEEN THROUGH TO GET BACK *HOME?* ARE YOU *SURE?*

SNOOB WILL ALWAYS BE *SPECIAL* TO ME, BUT HOME IS MORE THAN JUST WHERE YOU ARE *FROM.*

HOME IS WHERE YOU *BELONG.*

I LOVE MY BROTHER AND WE HAVE PROMISED TO VISIT EACH OTHER MORE OFTEN, BUT WHERE I BELONG--WHERE I TRULY FEEL *MOST* AT HOME--

THE END!

Disney

CLASSIC STORIES RETOLD
WITH THE MAGIC OF DISNEY!

Disney Treasure Island, starring Mickey Mouse

Robert Louis Stevenson's classic tale of pirates, treasure, and swashbuckling adventure comes to life in this adaptation!

978-1-50671-158-4 ✠ $10.99

Disney Moby Dick, starring Donald Duck

In an adaptation of Herman Melville's classic, sailors venture out on the high seas in pursuit of the white whale Moby Dick.

978-1-50671-157-7 ✠ $10.99

Disney Hamlet, starring Donald Duck

The ghost of a betrayed king appoints Prince Ducklet to restore peace to his kingdom in this adaptation of William Shakespeare's tragedy.

978-1-50671-219-2 ✠ $10.99

Disney Don Quixote, starring Goofy & Mickey Mouse

A knight-errant and the power of his imagination finds reality in this adaptation of the classic by Miguel de Cervantes!

978-1-50671-216-1 ✠ $10.99